The Gambling Habit

Pete Guppy

RISING ★ STARS

in association with

nasen
Helping Everyone Achieve

NASEN House, 4/5 Amber Business Village, Amber Close, Amington,
Tamworth, Staffordshire B77 4RP

Rising Stars UK Ltd.
22 Grafton Street, London W1S 4EX
www.risingstars-uk.com

Text © Rising Stars UK Ltd.

The right of Pete Guppy to be identified as the author of this work has
been asserted by him in accordance with the Copyright, Design and
Patents Act, 1988.

Published 2009

Cover design: Roger Warham
Cover image: Jupiterimages/Brand X/Alamy
Text design and typesetting: Roger Warham
Publisher: Gill Budgell
Editorial consultant: Lorraine Petersen

British Library Cataloguing in Publication Data.

A CIP record for this book is available from the British Library.

ISBN: 978-1-84680-596-7

Printed in the UK by CPI Bookmarque, Croydon, CR0 4TD

Mixed Sources
Product group from well-managed
forests and other controlled sources
www.fsc.org Cert no. TT-COC-002227
© 1996 Forest Stewardship Council

Chapter

The starter's flag was up. The hare was on its way. The dogs were barking in the traps. Steve was at the start with his fingers crossed.

He'd put his last £10 on number 6, and he needed a win. If he won, he could keep on betting. If he lost, he was in trouble.

The hare flashed past him.

The flag went down and the traps opened. Six dogs leapt out and went racing down the track.

They were long and fast. Their backs seemed to bend in two as they reached top speed. Number 6 was fastest out of the traps but the rest were right on his tail.

"Go on, Lucky Boy!" shouted Steve.

"Go on, Black Jack!" shouted someone in the crowd.

Number 6 was still in the lead as they went down the back straight. Steve could see his £10 bet turning into a £50 win.

"Go on, Lucky Boy. Keep going!" he yelled.

But as they raced into the next bend, number 3 came up alongside Lucky Boy. Then number 4 came up on the outside and took the lead. With 150 metres to go, the crowd were going mad.

"Come on, Swift Rose!" shouted some of them.

"Come on, Black Jack!" shouted others.

Steve jumped up and down, yelling his head off. "Hang on, Lucky Boy. You can do it!"

The three of them were together as they came round the last bend. The dogs stretched out their long legs to grab at the next bit of track. Their eyes were fixed on the hare.

"Go on, Lucky Boy!" screamed Steve, as the dogs flashed past him.

There were still 60 metres to go and the crowd standing at the finish were going crazy.

Steve could only stand and watch as the dogs reached the line. The race was over.

Some people jumped for joy. Some put their heads in their hands. Some tore up their tickets.

Steve was too far away to see which dog had won. All he could do was wait and see which numbers came up on the big board at the end of the track.

It seemed a long wait. It had been a close race and the judges were taking their time.

"Please let me win. If I win I'll never, ever, bet again," he lied to himself.

At last the numbers came up, 6-4-3. Lucky Boy had won, Swift Rose was second and Black Jack was third.

Steve put his fists in the air and shouted, "Yes!" He'd won £50, plus the £10 bet he'd put on.

But he couldn't go down to the bookmaker to get his money. He was only 14 and too young to bet. That's why he'd come to the track with Andy.

Andy was 19 and knew a lot about betting and gambling.

"Who's a lucky boy, then?" said Andy, as he handed Steve his winnings.

Steve smiled at the joke. Then he put the £60 in his pocket as fast as he could.

"You're forgetting something," said Andy.

"I'll pay you later," said Steve.

"You'll pay me now. That's £10 for putting all your bets on. And £10 for getting you into this place," said Andy.

Steve handed over the money. "I've got time for one more race. I want to put £10 to win on Dream Flyer," he said. Andy took the money for the two-lap race.

Steve had to be home for 9.30 p.m. He'd told his mum and dad he was doing his homework at his mate's house. If he wasn't back on time, he knew his mum would ring up to check on him.

Lying to his parents was risky. But Steve was willing to risk everything to keep on gambling.

Betting on dogs, betting on horses, playing the slot machines. He was hooked.

Steve watched the six greyhounds being led out for the next race. Each one had a number and a muzzle. The dogs had a spring in their step, as if they couldn't wait to start running.

Steve walked over to look at the betting odds on a bookmaker's board. Dream Flyer was at 5 to 1. Little Imp was 7 to 1. Soft Silk and Speedy Ted were 4 to 1. Fast Finish and Flashy Driver were 3 to 1. If Dream Flyer won, he'd be putting another £50 in his pocket.

He stood watching the bookmakers take bets. Some people bet £2, some bet £5. One man put £100 on Soft Silk.

"I bet that's the winner," Steve said to himself.

With two minutes to go, the dogs were put into the traps.

Dream Flyer didn't want to go in so she was given a push. Then around came the hare and away went the dogs

Dream Flyer was last out of the traps, and still last going into the first bend. "Get a _____ move on," Steve swore out loud.

He got a look from the woman next to him. Dream Flyer must have heard him as well because she moved up into third place.

"That's better!" yelled Steve. As the dogs started the last lap it was Soft Silk 1st, Little Imp 2nd and Dream Flyer 3rd. Steve pushed through the crowd to get to the finishing line.

Everyone was yelling and screaming as the dogs came round the last bend.

Soft Silk and Little Imp were now neck and neck, but Dream Flyer was catching them.

"Come on, come on," pleaded Steve.

With 50 metres to go, Dream Flyer found a bit more speed and lived up to her name. As the dogs flashed past the line, it was Dream Flyer by a nose from Soft Silk and Little Imp.

Steve jumped in the air with joy. Then he looked around for Andy, and his money. As he left the dog track to rush off home, Steve had £90 in his pocket and a smile on his face.

Like all gamblers, he felt he was born to win.

Chapter

2

He'd done it! He'd got away with it!
He'd lied to his parents and hadn't been
found out.

He'd been down to his last £10, but
come home with £90. He'd picked up his
school bag from behind the shed just
before walking into the house, and no one
had asked to see his homework.

Now all he had to do was think of a new excuse for his teachers.

"Let's see. What excuses have I used so far?" he said to himself.

1. My sister scribbled all over it.
2. I had to visit my grandma in hospital.
3. The dog ate it.
4. My sister ripped it up.
5. I had to visit my grandad in hospital.
6. We're moving house and my books got packed away.

"I need a new one," he said to himself. "It got put through the shredder by mistake. That'll do. They won't check up."

Steve got into bed and counted his money. The £90 was his passport to more gambling. He'd had fun winning on the dogs. Now he couldn't wait to play the slot machines again.

He slept with his winnings under his pillow and winning dreams in his head.

It was Saturday before he could play the slot machines at the arcade. He loved going there. The flashing lights and bleeping sounds seemed to pull him in off the street.

He couldn't wait to get started. But which machine should he start on? Pinball? Mad House? Cash Strike? Jiggin in the Riggin? He liked them all. Then he spotted a new one called Party Time.

"That's the one," he said to himself. Steve went to change a £10 note into coins. There was a new man in the cash booth.

"Are you 18?" he asked.

"Yes," lied Steve.

Then a voice said, "He's with me, and he's 18."

Steve turned round to see Andy standing by one of the machines.

"OK. If you say so," said the man.

Andy said, "You did well at the dogs.
I hope your luck holds out."

"It will," said Steve. And he started playing
Party Time. As soon as he put money into the
machine he seemed to go into another
world. His school reports said he couldn't
keep his mind on one thing for long. If only
his teachers could see him now.

For two hours he didn't take his eyes off
the machines. He pressed the buttons and
played with skill. Sometimes he held.
Sometimes he nudged. Sometimes he took
a chance. All the time he watched the wheels
spin round hoping to hear the sound of
money spilling out.

But these were greedy machines. They
took more money than they gave back. They
had to. They're made that way. Gamblers
know this but they choose to forget. Steve
went from slot machine to slot machine.

He changed one £10 note after another. At first, he won more than he lost. Pinball paid out £4. Mad House paid out £8. Cash Strike paid out £10. But he fed all his winnings back in. He played until his pockets were empty. £90 was gone in two hours! It was a shock to him.

Up until now he'd been a winner and gambling had been fun. Now his money had gone and it hurt to stop playing.

He looked in his pockets. Then he looked in the trays of the machines. Maybe some coins had been left in them. But his luck had run out. All he could do was stand and watch other people still playing the machines. The fun had gone.

But if Steve had looked around he would have seen that no one was having fun in this place. There were no smiles on faces. No one cheered, or clapped, or shouted if they won.

There were just lonely people feeding coin after coin into machines that would beat them in the end.

But Steve was hooked. Gambling was in his blood. He knew he'd be back.

All he had to do was work out where he could get his hands on some more money.

Chapter

3

Steve picked up the iPod his mum and dad had given him. He'd had a lot of fun with it. But it had to go. He could get good money for it. And he did. He sold it at school. Then he sold his best trainers, his skateboard, his DVDs, Nintendo and his phone.

The kids at school called him 'The Boot Sale Kid'.

They even sent him a note in Maths saying,

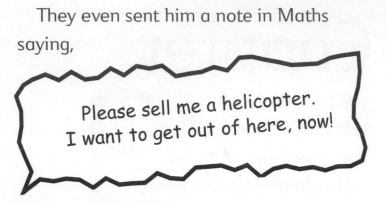

Please sell me a helicopter.
I want to get out of here, now!

It all made sense to Steve. The more money he got, the more gambling he could do. But he was telling more and more lies to his parents. He told them he'd lent his iPod and skateboard to a friend. That he'd lost his trainers at a football match. That he was swapping his Nintendo. That he had sold his DVDs to get money to buy a present for a friend. And that he had lost his phone, but didn't know where or when.

Lies were being stacked on lies. But it didn't matter to him as long as he could keep on gambling and keep hoping for that big win.

But the big win didn't happen, and he soon had nothing left to sell.

So to help feed his gambling habit he went without food at lunchtimes.

His dinner money got him into card games with Year 12 kids.

He also made money by doing homework for Year 7 kids. His parents didn't suspect a thing. When he was upstairs, they said, "It's good to see him getting down to his homework."

When he was out playing the slot machines, they said, "It's good to see him making new friends."

But these friends were loud and flashy, and took his money. He lied for them. Then he began stealing for them as well. He took coins out of his mum's purse. Then he started taking a note when she had a few of them. He did the same with his dad's wallet. He even stole from his gran.

His need to gamble was so strong, it didn't matter who he stole from, or lied to. The more he gambled, the more he lost.

He was just putting the last of his coins into a slot machine, when Andy came over.

"Hi Steve. How's the gambling going?" he asked, as he counted a roll of money.

"Not so good. But I feel lucky. I just need a bit of money to keep me going," said Steve. This was just what Andy had been waiting to hear and he peeled off five £20 notes from his roll.

"I'll tell you what I'll do," he said. "I've seen the way you play. You're good. It's just a matter of time before you get a big payout." He handed the five notes to Steve. "Take this and pay me back next week," he said.

It was just what Steve wanted to hear. He took the money and kept playing. Just like Andy, the slot machines played Steve for the fool he was. Pinball paid out £20 on the first night. Cash Strike paid out £18 and Party Time £9 on the next night.

But his winning streak didn't last. By the end of the week, he was keeping out of Andy's way. It didn't do him any good. Andy met up with him on his way home from school.

"So where's my money?" asked Andy.

"It's at home. I didn't want to take it to school. I'll pay you tomorrow," said Steve.

"But if it's at home, I'll come and get it now," said Andy.

"No. There's no one in at home and I've forgotten my key," said Steve. Andy reached his hand into Steve's pocket and took out a key.

"You mean this one?" he said. Steve knew he was beaten.

"Look. I haven't got your money. I had a bit of bad luck," he said.

Andy smiled, but his voice didn't.

"You've got until next Saturday to come up with the money. Or your gambling days will be over," he said.

"What do you mean?" asked Steve.

"I mean your parents will find out about your little habit," said Andy.

"No. They mustn't find out. They'd stop me gambling," pleaded Steve. The panic in Steve's voice made Andy smile.

"Well then. You and I need to have a little chat. I've got a plan that will get you winning again," said Andy.

Chapter

"But that's shoplifting!" said Steve.

"You don't have to lift up the shop. You just have to take things out of it," joked Andy. Steve didn't think the joke was funny.

"What if I get caught? What would happen to me?" asked Steve.

"You won't get caught. You'll have me and Mike to help you," said Andy.

Steve still looked shocked.

Andy said, "It's easy. I tell you the things I want. You go shopping and forget to pay. I sell the things you bring me. You get paid and soon pay off the £100 you owe me. Then you keep on working for me and get the money you need for gambling."

Steve didn't know what to say.

"You do want to keep on gambling, don't you?" asked Andy.

Steve nodded his head. "It's the best feeling in the world," he said.

Andy smiled to himself. He'd reeled Steve in like a fish on a line.

"You need to keep on gambling and I need my £100 back. So what do you say to my little plan?" asked Andy.

Steve couldn't see another way out. "How do I do it?" he asked.

On Saturday afternoon, Steve was in a shop on the High Street.

His heart was pounding. He'd been told what to do. Now it was up to him. He felt everyone was looking at him as if they knew what he was going to do.

But his need to gamble kept him going. He walked slowly round the shop. Then quickly put a watch in his pocket. Walking out of the shop seemed to last forever. "Don't rush," he kept telling himself.

At last, he was outside and round the corner of the next street. He met Mike who took the watch from him and walked off with it.

Steve went to the park with his head spinning and his legs feeling weak. He flopped down on a park bench and waited for Andy.

"You were good," said Andy, as he sat down next to Steve. "I was watching you from across the street. You kept your cool and didn't panic."

"I felt as if I was going to be sick and wet myself at the same time," said Steve.

"That's OK. It was your first time. The more you do it, the easier it'll get," said Andy.

"I don't think I can do it again," said Steve.

"Oh yes you can. You still owe me money," said Andy. "And don't you forget it."

So Steve began stealing for Andy. The more shoplifting he did, the better he got. He used magnets and a bag lined with tin foil to stop the security tags from making a noise. He took off security tags with a screwdriver.

He became good at picking up lots of clothes and running like mad. Sometimes Mike was there to help him. Sometimes he worked on his own.

Andy kept telling him, "The shops are

asking for it. If they don't want things stolen they should keep them locked up in a glass case."

Steve paid back the £100. Then he went on stealing so he could start gambling again.

As gambling was his life, life seemed very good indeed. But he was forgetting one thing. Shopkeepers hate shoplifters and try very hard to catch them.

Steve was in a shop he thought he knew well. He stood with his back to the camera and put some wallets in his pocket. But he didn't see the new camera, or the shop-keeper lock the door.

"Not so fast, you," said the shopkeeper, as Steve tried to open the door. "I saw you put those wallets in your pocket. I've got you on film."

Steve acted quickly. He put the wallets on the counter and said, "I'll pay you for them if you give me time."

"You'll pay all right. If I had my way I'd kick you round this shop. But all I can do is hand you over to the police," said the shopkeeper.

"Please, don't do that. They'll tell my parents," begged Steve.

"You should have thought of that before you started stealing," he said.

"Please, I'll never steal again if you let me go," pleaded Steve.

"Well, hard luck. I've heard that one before. I'm fed up with shoplifters. I'm not letting you go. I'm calling the police," said the shopkeeper.

And he did. Steve was taken to the police station. A phone call was made to his mum and dad. They came and listened to the police tell Steve that if he stole again, he could be spending time away from home.

His mum and dad were angry and ashamed.

His gran told him to 'sort himself out'.
His teachers told him it was for the best
and he could now make a fresh start.

Steve listened to them all. He looked
upset when the police spoke to him.
He looked sad when his mum and dad
spoke to him. He nodded his head at the
right times when his teachers spoke to him.

Two weeks later he was gambling again,
losing again and shoplifting again!

There seemed to be no stopping him.
Then fate took a hand.

Chapter 5

From under the peak of his cap, Steve was checking for cameras in a new shop in town.

He had chains and bracelets on his shopping list. He was just about to pocket some chains when he saw her.

She was wearing jeans and a vest top. Her long brown hair was tied in a ponytail. A white bag was hanging over her shoulder.

Steve didn't think he liked girls. But he liked this one. This one made him stand and stare.

She made his eyes open even more when she put a bottle of perfume into her white bag. She was shoplifting!

But in that split second, he also saw that a shop assistant had spotted her as well. Steve was over by the girl's side in a flash.

"Put it back. You've been seen," he hissed into her ear.

"You what?" she said. Steve reached into her bag and put the bottle back on the shelf.

"Come on. Play it cool. Just walk out of the shop. They can't do anything. They've got no proof," said Steve. But as the two of them got to the door the manager was waiting for them.

"What have you got in the bag?" he asked.

"Why? Do you want to use my hair brush?" said the girl.

"I'd like you to show me what you've got in your bag," he said, keeping his temper.

"No," said the girl.

"Right. I think you've been shoplifting and I'm calling the police," he said. He started walking her to the counter.

"Let me go. Get off me, you big bully!" she shouted.

Steve didn't like the way this was going. Meeting the police again was not what he wanted. Something had to be done.

Steve grabbed the bag off the girl and turned it upside down on the counter. He hoped she hadn't been stealing other things as well as the bottle of perfume. She had! And they all came falling out onto the counter.

As the shopkeeper reached out to catch the stolen goods, he let go of the girl. Steve pulled her away and shouted, "Come on! Run for it!"

So they did; out of the shop, down the street, across the road into a shopping mall, out the other side and into a small park. Then they flopped down onto a bench to get their breath back.

Steve still liked what he saw. Up until now, girls were just people you sometimes had to sit next to in class. This girl was different. He'd pay to sit next to her. Well, he would if his mates weren't around!

Steve was feeling good about himself. He'd risked his neck to save this girl. She'd want to thank him. He might even get his first kiss. She turned her lovely face to him and said, "You prat! What did you do that for? Why did you empty my bag?"

Steve felt shocked and hurt. "I was trying to help you. I didn't think you'd put most of the shop in your bag," he said.

"That's the problem with boys. You've got nothing to think with," she said.

Steve's shock was turning to anger. "I risked my neck for you," he said.

"Nobody asked you to," she said. Steve forgot about his first kiss.

"So how would you have got out of the mess you were in?" he asked.

"I'd have found a way," she said

"What would you have done?" he asked.

"Something," she said.

"What?" asked Steve.

The girl grabbed her bag and stood up. "Oh, shut up. I don't need your help. Just stay out of my way," she said.

As she went off, Steve shouted, "I'll stay out of your way. I wouldn't help you again if you paid me." But he knew he was lying. He knew he'd help her, if she needed it. And she did.

Just as she was leaving the park a lad grabbed her by the arm. He yelled and shook her at the same time.

Then he slapped her and walked off. Steve ran over to her. The girl was sitting on a bench, crying. He sat down and put his arm round her.

She pushed him away and said, "Don't start that. I can look after myself, thank you."

"It didn't look like it just now," he said.

"I can handle it. So push off," she said.

She dried her eyes and stood up to go. Steve pulled her down onto the bench.

"I'm not going until you tell me what's going on," he said.

"It's got nothing to do with you. I told you, just push off," she said. She tried to get up but Steve stopped her.

"What's going on? Why were you shoplifting? And why is he pushing you around?" he asked.

The girl took a deep breath, "He's my boyfriend. He's on drugs and needs money to pay for them," she said.

"I do the shoplifting and he sells the stuff I steal. If I make a mess of things, he gets angry."

"Why don't you leave him?" asked Steve.

"I've tried. But he pleads with me to come back. He tells me he'll give up drugs, but he doesn't," she said.

"Why don't you tell your parents?" asked Steve.

"They'd go mad. They'd stop me seeing him. He says he loves me. But I'm a bit frightened of him," she said.

Steve didn't know what to say. He knew about gambling, but not much about love.

"If he loves you, he'll give up drugs and stop hitting you," he said.

The girl looked at him and smiled.

"It's not that easy," she said.

Then Steve spoke without thinking. "I'd give up drugs for you," he said. He could feel himself getting hot, and he knew he was blushing. He wanted the ground to open up so he could hide.

"That's sweet of you," said the girl.

Steve didn't want to be sweet. He wanted to get her boyfriend by the neck and pull his head off.

"You can't keep letting him beat you up. And you've got to stop shoplifting," he said.

"I know. But how?" she asked.

Chapter 6

A week later, Steve found a way to help the girl. He was walking the long way home from school, hoping to see her in the park again. He didn't know her name but he had been thinking about her all week.

Then he saw her, and his heart missed a beat. She was sitting in the park with her boyfriend.

Steve stopped. Should he keep going, and walk right by them? His heart wasn't missing a beat now. It was racing like mad as he walked towards them.

As he got closer he heard her boyfriend say, "Do as you're told. You know I need the money. So just get into the shops."

"But you keep on telling me you're going to stop taking that stuff. So why don't you stop?" she asked.

Her boyfriend jumped to his feet and grabbed hold of her. "I can't stop. Not yet," he said. The girl tried to get away but he twisted her arm and she cried out in pain.

Steve was now so close that they turned and looked at him.

The boyfriend said, "What are you looking at? It's got nothing to do with you. So_____ off."

Steve didn't move, but words jumped out of his mouth. "Let go of her," he said.

"_____off," said the boyfriend.

Steve got into his first fight. He grabbed hold of the boyfriend and pulled him away from her. Then he hit him as hard as he could. Before he could think or blink, Steve hit him again. The boyfriend fell to the ground. His nose was bleeding.

Steve stood over him and said, "If you ever hurt her again, I'll come after you." The boyfriend got to his feet and wiped his hand across his face. He pointed to the girl and said, "You're still my girl. Don't you forget that." Then he limped away across the grass. Like all bullies, he could dish it out but he couldn't take it.

Steve sat down on the bench. He wasn't used to fighting. His legs felt weak, his fist hurt, and his head was spinning.

He looked up at the girl and said, "Well, do you want to be free of him?"

"Yes, I do," she said.

Then she sat down and said, "Thanks. You were great. What's your name?"

"It's Steve. What's yours?" he said.

"Emma," she said.

Emma picked up Steve's hand and held it. Then she leaned over and kissed him. He liked it. But then he looked around to see if anyone was looking. There wasn't. So he went back for his second kiss, and it lasted longer this time.

Emma said, "If we keep on doing this, I think you could get good at it."

Steve didn't know what to say, or think. His head was spinning and his legs felt weak again. But for a different reason this time.

Emma said, "It was lucky you saw me in that shop last week. What were you buying in there?"

"I wasn't. I was shoplifting," said Steve. Emma was up on her feet in a flash.

"You were what?" she asked.

"I was doing the same as you," said Steve.

"Why were you shoplifting?" Emma asked in a loud voice.

Steve pulled her back down onto the bench. "Not so loud. I don't want the whole town to know," he said.

"So why were you shoplifting?" she asked in a softer voice.

Steve told her everything. Well, nearly everything. He left out the bit about stealing from his gran.

"Are you going to stop gambling?" asked Emma.

"I don't know. I get a buzz out of it," he said.

"If it's a buzz you're after, maybe I can help," said Emma. Then she leaned over and kissed him again. It was a long time before they came up for air.

Steve felt great. He'd just won a fight.

He'd saved Emma from having to steal.
And he liked what she was doing.

"Well, do you think you can give up
gambling and shoplifting?" asked Emma,
again.

Saying no to Emma wasn't what Steve
had in mind right now.

"Yes. I can give them up," he said.

And he did, for a time.

Chapter 7

Steve finished with gambling and
shoplifting, and started with Emma.
Overnight, he changed. He found out
where the shower was.

"Why have you started washing?" his
little sister asked him. He got a hair cut
that made him look harder. He splashed
his dad's aftershave all over himself.

He even put some under his arms. You could smell him two streets away.

"I don't buy that stuff by the bucketful, you know," his dad said.

He brushed his teeth. And he did his homework. He was making a fresh start. Steve's mum and dad were pleased. His teachers were pleased. His gran said to him, "I knew it would take a girl to sort you out."

He stopped all the things that had made him money at school. He didn't have time for all of that. His time and pocket money were spent on Emma. They went tenpin bowling and Emma won every game. Steve got into a bad mood. Then Emma slipped her hand into his on the way home and he forgot all about the game.

They went to the pictures, where they sat on the back row and had fun in the dark. They didn't see much of the films.

They went to McDonald's, where Emma held a chip between her lips and Steve nibbled it from the other end. That was from one bit of a film they had seen.

They went swimming, where Steve saw more of Emma than he'd seen before. She took his breath away. They did a lot of splashing, chasing and catching.

They went to the park, where they walked and talked, stopped and kissed, sat and cuddled.

They went ice-skating, where they had to hold on to each other in case they fell. But Steve had already fallen. He'd fallen in love with Emma.

They talked for hours on the phone at home. It was after one of these long calls that Steve's dad had a word with him about girls.

"You see, Steve. When I was young, I had girlfriends. So I know what it's like," he said.

"But you've got to be careful. You know what I mean?"

"No," lied Steve. He'd been to all the lessons about sex at school. But he wanted to see his dad struggle.

"Well, it's like this," his dad said. "When you're out with girls, things can happen."

"What things?" asked Steve.

"Things can get a bit out of hand," said his dad.

"Out of hand? What did you have in *your* hand when you went out with your girlfriends?" asked Steve, trying not to smile.

"I didn't have anything in my hand," said his dad.

"So, what can get out of my hand?" asked Steve, trying not to laugh.

"I'm not talking about *your* hand," said his dad.

"Yes, you were. You said things can get out of hand," said Steve.

"Look, I'll start again," said his dad, who was now going red and wishing he'd never started this little chat.

"It's just that, when a boy and girl get together, well. . ."

His dad didn't know what to say next. Steve helped him out by saying, "You mean, if we have sex I should wear a condom." His dad's mouth fell open. Steve got out of the room as fast as he could.

His dad wasn't the only one wanting to have a word with him about Emma. Most of his mates had something to say as well!

"Saw you snogging that girl last night," said Kate.

"How far did you get?" asked Zak.

"Will you have to marry her now?" asked Preeya.

"Do you want a packet of three?" asked Rick.

His Maths teacher didn't help when she said, "Someone in this room smells nice, today."

"It's Steve, Miss. He's got his before-shave on," said Mandip.

"You mean, aftershave," said Miss Burns.

"No, Miss. He hasn't started shaving yet," said Mandip. The class fell around laughing.

Steve didn't let any of this get to him. He'd had one fight to win Emma. He didn't want another one if he could help it.

Anyway, Emma was hot. He was proud to be her boyfriend. He'd never met anyone like her. She made him laugh. She helped him talk about things. She looked great, she smelt great. She made him go weak at the knees.

And she'd saved him from gambling.
Or had she?

Having the gambling bug is like having an illness. Sometimes, just when you think you've got rid of it, it comes back. It did with Steve.

He was waiting for Emma one night after they had been tenpin bowling. He put one coin into a slot machine and it started him off again.

Soon, more coins were going into machines when Emma wasn't around. There was less money in his pocket when he wanted to take her out for the night.

But like all gamblers, Steve was greedy. He wanted the best of both worlds. So he went back to shoplifting and working with Andy.

Emma spotted the change in him. He started turning up late and lying about where he'd been. Sometimes he had too much money with him. Sometimes he had none at all.

"You've started gambling again, haven't you?" she asked. Steve said nothing.

"And you're shoplifting again, aren't you?" she asked. Steve just looked away from her.

"You're a fool if you go back to all that," she said.

"It'll be OK. You wait and see," said Steve. But it wasn't OK.

Chapter

8

Steve had the two things he most wanted in life, his girl and his gambling. He was on a lucky streak and he felt it would last forever.

But his luck ran out on the day he was seen stealing leather jackets and trying to run out of the shop. Bells rang and an angry shopkeeper rang the police. This time Steve got more than just a telling off.

This time the police charged him with stealing goods and he was sent to court.

There were tears of anger and dismay at home. His teachers shook their heads. His gran wouldn't see him. Emma called him a prat, but she didn't dump him.

On the day he went to court he wore his smartest clothes and his best smile. But that didn't fool them for a second.

They heard what he had been up to and asked him how often he had been shoplifting. Then they put him on a Referral Order for six months.

The Order was like getting a yellow card at football. If he'd been given a red card, he would have been sent away from home for 12 months.

The Referral Order let him live at home and still go to school. But he would have to come face to face with some of the shopkeepers he had stolen from.

He had to meet and talk to them. Then they would have a say in what would happen to him. Steve could feel himself start to sweat.

One shopkeeper had wanted to kick him round the shop. What would the others want to do to him? A week later, he found out. There were six of them and they asked him a lot of questions.

"Why did you steal from us?"

"What did you steal?"

"How many shops did you steal from?"

"What did you do with the money you made?"

"How do you think your mum and dad feel?" Steve had to answer all the questions.

Then came the big question, "How did you sell the things you stole?" Steve didn't know what to say. He didn't want to talk about Andy.

The policeman in the room said, "Come on, Steve. Tell us who you were working for." Steve didn't speak.

The policeman said, "I'm going to say a name. All you have to do is tell me if I'm right." Steve looked across at the policeman.

"Andy Wood. Andy Wood sells the stolen goods. Am I right, Steve?" he asked.

Steve still didn't say anything.

The policeman looked at Steve's face. He smiled and said, "I'll get him, one day."

Then came the last question from the shopkeepers, "How do you feel about what you have done?"

Steve looked at the faces of the shopkeepers. He knew he wouldn't get away with lying to them. So he didn't try.

"I don't feel anything. I needed some money, so I stole it. Then I needed more, so I stole again."

It wasn't what they wanted to hear. They talked it over after he had left the room.

"He's not even sorry," said one.

"All he thinks about is himself," said another.

"He's treating our shops like a bank."

"Gambling has taken hold of his life."

"He needs to spend more time with people and less time with slot machines." They talked it over some more with the policeman who was in charge of Steve. Then they came up with a plan.

Steve was going to work for two hours a week with children in a special school. A police officer would take him to a residential school every Monday evening, for six months.

Steve smiled when he was told. "That doesn't sound too bad," he said to himself. But he had the biggest shock of his life waiting for him.

His first visit to the school was like walking into a different world. A world full of disabilities. Some of the children had been born without arms, some without legs. Some struggled to speak and others couldn't talk at all. Some couldn't stop dribbling and some had a head that seemed far too big.

It was a world of wheelchairs and walking frames. Of jerky movements and being helped to eat. It was a world of people who looked very different from how he looked. And he didn't like it.

The first two hours seemed like a lifetime. He wanted to get away from the place as fast as he could, and not come back. He knew he shouldn't feel like this, but he did. He wanted out.

"I can't come here for the next six months. I'll do something else, but I'm not coming back here," he told the officer who was with him.

"Your Order says you'll come here, and here is where you'll come. You don't get to choose," said the officer.

"But why here? Why can't I be with normal people? Why wasn't I sent to sweep shop floors or clean shop windows? It was shoplifting I was doing," said Steve.

"Why do you think you've been sent here?" asked the officer.

"I'm asking you," said Steve, angrily.

"Well, maybe it's time you started asking yourself a few questions," said the officer.

Steve found the second visit just as hard. He couldn't bring himself to mix with anyone. He didn't want to be seen with them. So he just sat at the back of the room and watched five kids playing cards.

A kid in a wheelchair was dealing, and every bit of him shook as he struggled to hand out the cards. Some cards flew out of his hand. It took him ages to pick them up and put them back in the pack. He was worn out by the time he'd finished.

Then there was a lot of chatter and laughter as the game started. Steve couldn't make out what some of them were saying but they were all having fun. One or two found it hard to put their cards down on the table.

Steve was watching a girl who only had one small finger and thumb on each hand. He couldn't work out how she did so well. She must have seen him watching, because at the end of the game she turned her wheelchair round and came over to him. Steve wanted to get away but she was across the room in a flash.

"You've been sitting here for a long time. Do you want to play?" she asked.

"No thanks," said Steve.

"Are you shy, or don't you like us?" she asked.

Steve didn't know what to say. He had the feeling she knew the answer.

The girl held out her hand and said, "My name's Donna. Welcome to Three Oaks School."

Steve looked at the small finger and thumb. He knew he should try to shake hands with her, but he couldn't do it.

Time seemed to stand still as they looked at each other. Then Donna reached over and took hold of his hand. Steve felt his fingers curl round her small finger and thumb as they shook hands.

"Please come and play cards with us," she said.

"I can't play cards," he lied.

Donna kept hold of his hand and looked into his eyes. "We'll show you," she said.

Chapter 9

"Come on. Come and meet my friends,"
said Donna, as she tugged at Steve's hand.
Steve got to his feet and walked beside
Donna's wheelchair as she led him to the
card game.

"I don't know your name," she said.

"It's Steve," he said.

Donna told him the names of the players.

There was Tom, Sandeep, Becky and Jack. They all looked up and said, "Hi."

Donna said, "We're going to try a new card game that someone showed me. It's called Ponteam, or something like that."

"Pontoon," said Steve, without thinking.

"That's not bad for someone who can't play cards," said Donna.

Steve went hot all over. "I think I might have played it a long time ago," he lied.

Donna smiled but didn't say anything. She shuffled the cards and began dealing. Steve sat down and watched her.

He couldn't take his eyes off her hands. He was amazed how well she was doing. She gave each player two cards and told them the rules of the game.

Then she said, "So you have to get as close to 21 as you can. If you want another card from me, say twist. If you don't want a card, say stick."

The game started. And so did the fun. Tom tried picking up his cards too quickly and bent them. Sandeep had forgotten the rules. Becky kept cheating by looking at other people's cards. And Jack just kept saying twist because he liked getting more cards.

There was a lot of noise. Donna helped Sandeep, Tom shouted at Becky, and Jack kept shouting twist. Steve had never seen a game of cards like it. It was nothing like the games at school.

Then Donna said to Jack, "You can't keep having more cards. You've got more than 21 points. You've bust."

"Bust! Is that the same as tits?" shouted Jack.

Everyone fell around laughing. So did Steve. Donna tried to keep the game going, but it was no good. Every time someone went over 21, everyone shouted 'tits'. In the end, she stopped dealing.

She said to Steve, "Come on. This game is over for tonight. Let's go and get a drink."

They sat by the machine, drinking the cans. Donna said, "That wasn't too bad, was it?"

"What wasn't?" asked Steve.

"Playing cards with us," said Donna.

Before Steve could think what to say, two girls came by in wheelchairs.

"Is that your new boyfriend, Donna?" they asked. And they giggled as they went off.

Donna saw the look on Steve's face. "Don't panic. They're only joking," she said. Steve sat there not knowing what to say, or do. Donna said, "We may not look like you on the outside. But we're the same on the inside."

Steve drank from his can, not looking at her. Then Donna asked, "Are you going to come here every week?"

"Yes. Two hours a week for the next six months," said Steve.

"Why six months?" asked Donna.

Steve felt trapped again. Did he trust her with the truth or tell her more lies?

"It's a project I'm doing at school. We have to work with people and write about it," he lied.

"So your school sent you here?" asked Donna.

"Yes," lied Steve.

Donna raised her eyebrows and took another swig from her can.

"I know two people you can help," she said.

"Who?" asked Steve.

"Me, and Tom," said Donna. Steve looked puzzled.

"You can help me by joining in a card game each week. And Tom wants to write the story of his life so far," said Donna.

"But he can't read or write. He wants to put his story onto a computer."

"I know about computers," said Steve.

"Then you could be the man for the job. Tom can tell his story to you. You can write it down so he can type it letter by letter. He says it has to be him who does the typing. But some days his movements are so jerky he can't use the computer at all," said Donna.

"But I can't understand a word he says," said Steve.

Donna said, "I know it's not easy. But he really wants to get his story written. He'll keep on telling you what he's saying until you understand."

Donna had another swig of her drink. "Will you help us?" she asked.

"I'll try," said Steve.

"See you next week, then," she said. This time they both smiled as they shook hands.

The next week Steve joined in the game of cards. Becky still cheated. Sandeep still didn't know the rules. And Jack kept saying 'twist' so he could keep saying 'tits'. It was all good fun.

Steve asked Donna, "Why do you only play for matchsticks? Why don't you play for money?"

Donna said, "If we use money, someone always ends up getting upset. Money seems to get in the way of fun."

"You could be right," said Steve.

Then it was time to help Tom. The computer was switched on, and Donna left them to it.

Tom spoke as slowly as he could but Steve still couldn't understand him. They worked hard. But nothing was being written down and they were both getting fed up. Donna came to see how they were getting on.

"It's no good. I just can't understand what he's saying," said Steve.

Tom started jumping around in his chair and waving his arms.

"What's the matter?" asked Donna.

"Aneh. Geh Aneh," said Tom.

"Yes. Why didn't I think of that?" said Donna.

"What did he say?" asked Steve.

"Get Janet," said Donna. "She's the only one who can understand everything he says. They've known each other for years. But she soon gets fed up with things and then flies into a temper."

"Do you think she would help?" asked Steve.

"I don't know. She can't work at things for very long. I'll ask her before you come next week."

Chapter

10

Tom and Janet were waiting when Steve walked in the next week. Janet couldn't read or write very well but she could understand Tom. And she was willing to help.

The three of them got to work. Tom spoke to Janet. Janet told Steve. Steve wrote the words on paper.

Then Tom tried typing them into the computer. It was slow going.

Tom could only use one finger. And because of his disability his whole body shook as he tried to press the right key. He used a Big Key keyboard. But its was still hard work for him.

But he wouldn't give up. And he wouldn't let anyone do the typing for him. It was his story, and he was going to type it. After an hour he was worn out. It was time for a drink and a game of cards.

For the next ten weeks, Steve played cards and worked with Tom and Janet. Together they helped Tom write about his life. It wasn't a sad story. It was a story of hopes, and dreams, and plans. Tom wanted to watch sport, listen to rock bands, have a girlfriend, get a job and live in a house of his own one day.

As Tom struggled to type his story, Steve began to look at life in a different way.

He began to see what it was like to be trapped in a body that wouldn't do what you wanted it to do. He saw how hard some people have to work to be understood.

He began to understand how it must feel when people don't want to be seen with you because of the way you look.

He would never forget the last lines of Tom's story:

'Don't see wheelchairs. See people.
Don't see disabilities. See people.
Don't think, 'not normal'. Think people.'

At home, Steve began using the Internet to look for facts on disabilities. At school, he asked if he could do a project on children with disabilities. His lie to Donna was becoming the truth.

Everyone was pleased. Even his gran started talking to him again, but she called him Steven at first.

Steve had been taken to and from school in the car every day. He hadn't been let out at night, apart from going to Three Oaks School. And he hadn't seen Emma. He'd only spoken to her on the phone.

"Do you want to see Emma again?" asked his mum, one day.

"Yes," said Steve.

"We'd like to meet her as well. So how about asking her home for a meal?" said mum. So he did.

Bringing Emma home to meet his mum, dad and little sister wasn't going to be easy. When Emma rang the bell, Steve was first to the door. They got a hug and a kiss in before Steve's dad shouted from the kitchen, "Well, bring her in and let's have a look at her."

Steve groaned and took her in to meet them.

His little sister dashed in and said, "Is this your girlfriend then? Are you going to marry her?"

"Stop asking silly questions and sit down at the table," said his mum, quickly.

The Steve of old would have eaten his meal and gone out gambling. The new Steve chatted about his new friends.

"What will you do when you come to the end of your Referral Order?" asked his mum.

"I've told Donna that I'm going to keep visiting them. She still needs help showing them all sorts of games. Tom wants to keep getting better on the computer. And Janet says she wants to write her story as well," said Steve.

His mum and dad smiled at each other. But they had their fingers crossed.

When the meal was over, Steve took Emma upstairs to show her his room. His sister started to follow them, until their mum shouted, "Lisa. Back here, now!"

That left them alone to have an even bigger hug, and longer kiss. And they chatted about their hopes, dreams, and plans.

"But what about your gambling?" asked Emma.

"I've got too many other things to do," said Steve.

"Do you mean that?" asked Emma.

"You can bet on it," said Steve.

Look out for other exciting stories in the
Survival series:

About the author

Have you ever been hunted by the police, chased by a gang, or tried to stay alive after a plane crash?

If you have, then you know the name of the game is survival. If you haven't, why not read about the teenagers in my stories. They find getting into trouble is easy. It's the getting out of trouble that's the hard bit.

I spent three years training to be a teacher and 33 years being one.
I always wanted to know how hard it would be to write books for teenagers.
Now I know!

Pete Guppy

SURVIVAL

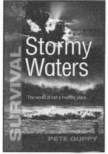